one woolly wombat

Written by Rod Trinca and Kerry Argent

Illustrated by Kerry Argent

An Omnibus/Puffin Book

one woolly wombat sunning by the sea
two cuddly koalas sipping gumnut tea
three warbling magpies waking up the sun
four thumping kangaroos dancing just for fun
five pesky platypuses splashing with their feet
six cheeky possums looking for a treat
seven emus running . . . in and out the bush
eight spiky echidnas eating ants — whoosh
nine hungry goannas wondering what to cook
ten giggly kookaburras writing riddle books
eleven dizzy dingoes twirling with their paws
twelve crazy cockatoos counting on their claws
thirteen hopping mice picking desert pea
fourteen slick seals sailing out to sea

one woolly wombat sunning by the sea

two cuddly koalas sipping gumnut tea

three warbling magpies waking up the sun

four thumping kangaroos dancing just for fun

five pesky platypuses splashing with their feet

six cheeky possums looking for a treat

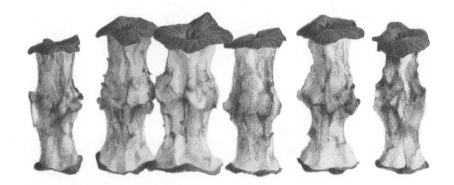

seven emus running . . . in and out the bush

eight spiky echidnas eating ants — whoosh

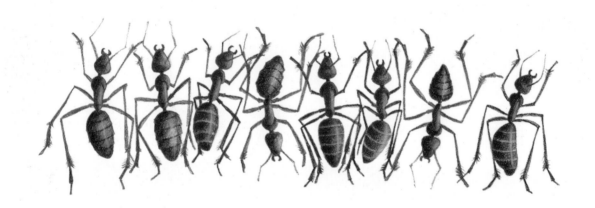

nine hungry goannas wondering what to cook

ten giggly kookaburras writing riddle books

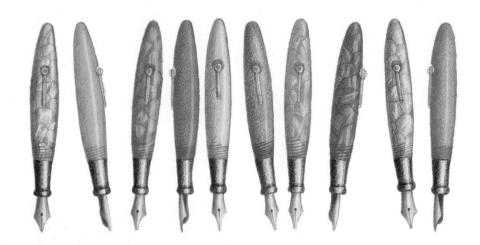

eleven dizzy dingoes twirling with their paws

twelve crazy cockatoos counting on their claws

thirteen hopping mice picking desert pea

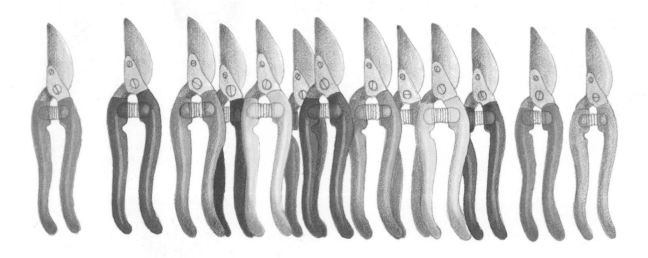

fourteen slick seals sailing out to sea